FROM A **TO** Z

Create your own meaningful artworks and messages with *From A to Z: Beautiful Letters to Colour and Share.*

Relax and be inspired as you create beautiful works of art from the pages of this book. Each letter has been especially created by talented hand-letterers and features a unique and intricate design that allows you to express your creativity.

This book features every letter of the alphabet, as well as additional versions of more common letters, so you have enough to create phrases like "Happy Birthday!" and "Congratulations!" It's possible that you'll still need extra letters, so simply photocopy the letters before you begin colouring. It is a good idea to keep a complete set of copies on hand so you know you will always have the letters you need!

ARTWORK INSPIRATION

There are many creative projects that can use your letters as a centrepiece. Some ideas include:

FRAMED LETTERS

Make a simple but stunning piece of art by framing the first letter of your name or the names of friends and family.

ALPHABET BUNTING

Create educational art for a child's room by attaching the letters A–Z to a long piece of twine with tape or mini craft pegs.

They'll marvel over all the different letters and patterns.

PARTY DECORATIONS AND CARDS

Why not make sensational decorations for your next gathering, such as a "Happy Birthday" or "Congratulations" banner? Making a unique decoration doesn't have to stop there - these letters are also perfect for making place settings. You could even go a step further and make a personalised birthday card!

INSPIRATIONAL WORDS AND PHRASES

Try creating wall art by choosing a word or phrase that inspires you, such as such as "Dream Big," "Live, Laugh, Love" or "Home Sweet Home." Putting these messages on a poster-size sheet and framing them can really bring the message home, is eye-catching and is a great conversational starter.

Ultimately you are only limited by your creativity. Whether you put your artworks on display or give them to someone special, sharing these creations will brighten everyone's day.

So enjoy the mindful tasks of colouring, papercraft and making meaningful messages.

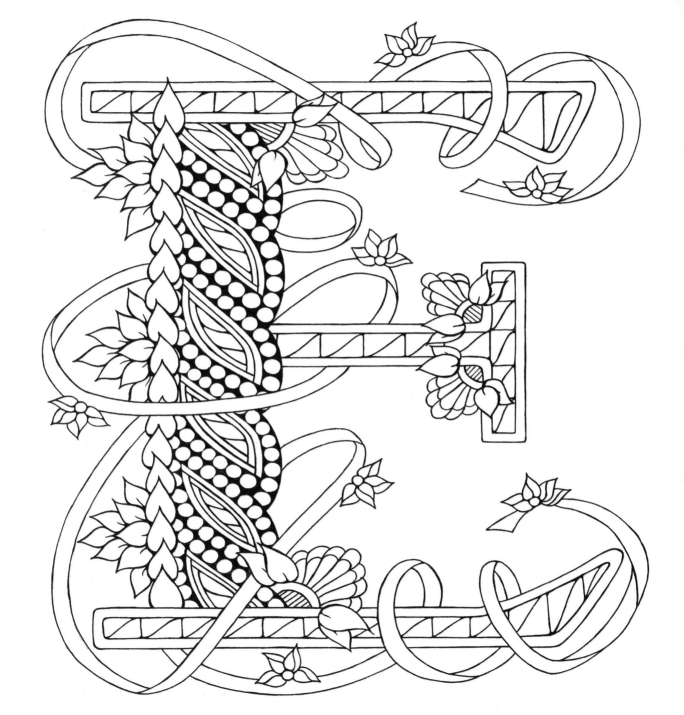